In the Land of Fear and Doubt

A collection of poems by

Ryan McCabe

With illustrations by Aidan Terry

All rights reserved. In accordance with the U.S. Copyright Act of 1976, the scanning, uploading, and electronic sharing of any part of this book without the permission of the publisher constitutes unlawful piracy and theft of the author's intellectual property. If you would like to use material from the book (other than for review purposes), prior written permission must be obtained by contacting the publisher at rpmccabe333@gmail.com.

"Digital Space," "The Bitter Bug," "The Office of Pillow and Sheets," "Nail-Biter Ned," and "Darewolves," were originally published in Redivider's issue 18.2 publication.

"Calvin Caught a Cloud" was originally published in Poetry Nation and Eber & Wein's anthology "Turning the Corner."

Thank you for your support of the author's rights.

ISBN 978-1-7331663-9-3

Dedicated to
Dean "the Locomotive" Lennert

In the Land of Fear and Doubt

LOST

CALVIN CAUGHT A CLOUD

Calvin ran down to the crick,
His fishing rod in hand,
And cast his bobber to the sky
Expecting something grand.
He closed his eyes and waited
For the lure to make a splash,
But no sound met his eardrums,
Yet the line began to thrash.
He dug his feet in, cranked the reel,
He pulled with all his might,
And when the fight was over
Stood awe-struck and ghostly white.
Calvin loved to fish
And any catch would make him proud,
But Calvin never thought
That he would one day catch a cloud!

GRIMM

The children left
A trail of crumbs
To help find their way home,
But in the woods
They should have known
That no one is alone.

THE BITTER BUG

The Bitter Bug has bitten down
And burrowed deep within
Prolonging pain by irritating
Scars beneath your skin.

It ruminates self-righteously
Upon its misery,
Unknowingly the victim
Of a self-made pillory.

Cocooned in anger
Vengeance masks emotional distress,
Impulses of revenge complete its
Metamorphosis.

To cure this parasite
Before it plagues your will to live,
The antidote I recommend
Is learn how to forgive.

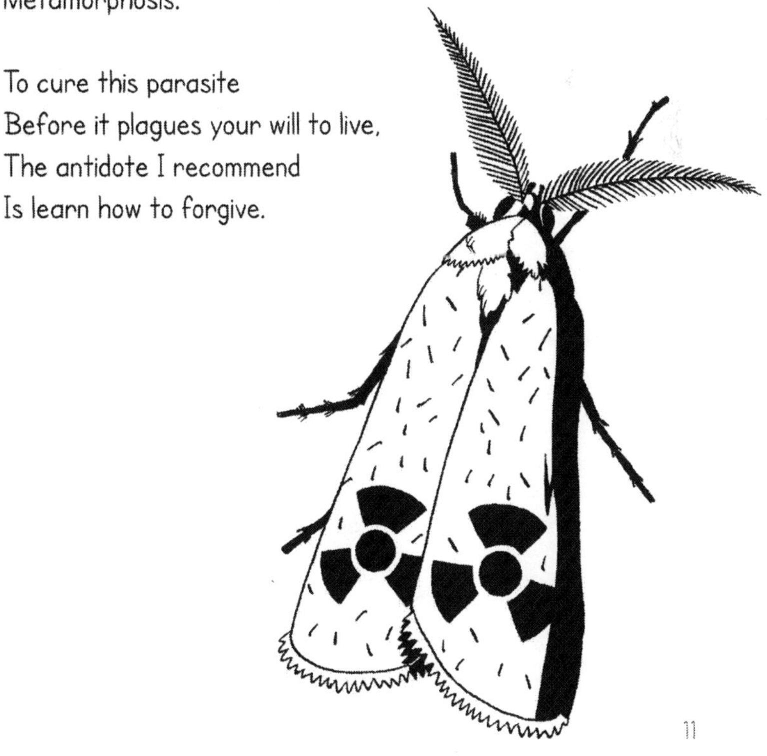

NAIL-BITER NED

His mother warned him.
"Ned," she said,
"Keep biting your nails
And you'll lose your head."
Did he listen?
Oh, no.
He just kept biting, so
He woke up one morning
And simply clipped,
"Whoa ..."

TRAVELING SALESMAN

If I were you, I wouldn't trust a single word I say,
But let me introduce myself. Dear friend, please call me Jay.
I'm in the field of selling lies, a rather sticky trade,
But business is a-boomin', for some people are afraid.
Afraid they're not enough or that the truth will hurt their friends.
Afraid to say the things they want, afraid of bitter ends.
Which brings me back to you, for I believe you've got the stuff.
I think you too can sell our wares, you're practiced well enough.
Please grab a pen and sign your name upon the dotted line.
Our fibbing frat will outfit you with clothing just like mine.
And then dear friend, you too shall travel door-to-door like me,
Preserving order with each sale to new signatories.
To tell the truth's a canker on the milieu of chitchat.
Discomfort stems from honesty. Believe me, that's a fact.
So do us all a favor: sign. I'll let you use my pen.
For once you do, the truth will never threaten you again.

IN FOR A PENNY

Sterling Pounds was eager to haggle
A bargain with any store clerk.
He strolled past the beggars who sat by his bank
And scoffed at them all like a jerk.
He hoarded his wealth in a brown leather chest
That he kept at the foot of his bed.
Each day he'd take stock of the earnings he made
From his ev'ry and each letterhead.
He never had time for his fam'ly or friends
He reluctantly saw them at all.
His mood rose and fell with each stock market swell,
All the rest simply seemed so banal.
Sterling Pounds, with his brown leather chest
And the contents he hoarded inside,
Lived in that box at the foot of his bed,
Which was also the place where he died.

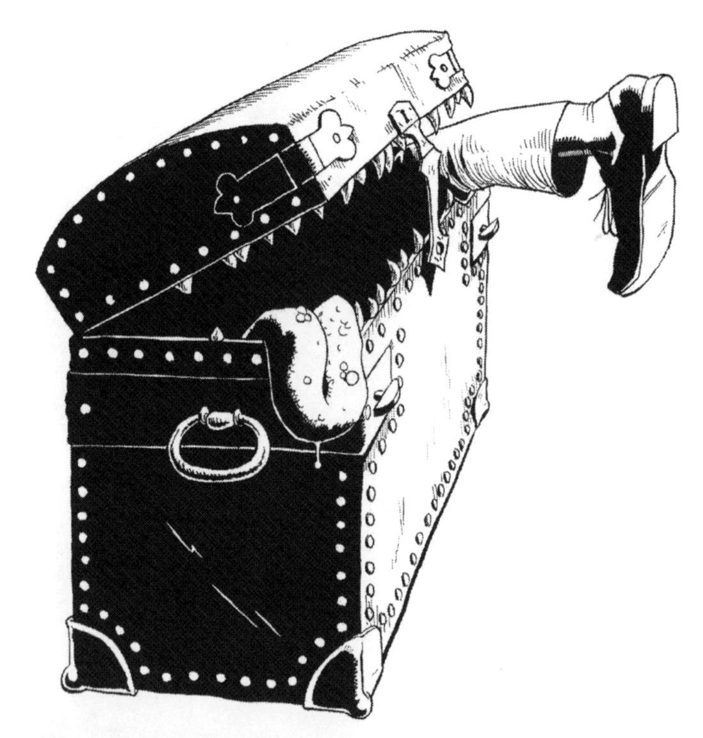

GRIFTER

Who
Stands
Atop the
Others? And
Who makes the
Bottom row? Who
Builds their life on top
Of strugglers, reaping what
They sow? Who looks to his or
Her neighbor, lusting for what they've
Got? Thinking I'll take what they have 'cept
The idiomatic pot? I'm at a loss for cheats and
Swindlers, frauds and grifters too. The kind who
Make their livelihood on those like me and you.

131

I went to dry my laundry
On a rooftop baked in sun,
A simple task that fastly
Found me in a conundrum.

Beside a plastic table
Were two groc'ry bags of booze.
Their contents evidence
Of a late-night and rowdy schmooze.

And underneath the table,
Folded to fit in one's jeans,
A stack of bills with Benjamin
Atop the other greens.

My first thought was to wait it out,
My laundry needed time.
Someone would come to claim their cash,
While I let my whites dry.

But time went on and no one came,
I sat beside the stack
And thought I'd make a flyer
Should the owner not come back.

A draft was ready. Control+P.
When it occurred to me,
What if they lied and said I took
From my discovery?

Do I believe this person
To be grateful, good and just?
Or do I fear that they're the type
To prey on others' trust?

I'm still up on my rooftop
And my clothing's long been done.
My mind is drenched in thought though,
What do you make of this one?

THE OFFICE OF PILLOW AND SHEETS

Why leave my bed?
Why leave at all?
With one quick click it's all resolved!

Fresh food delivered!
Content streamed!
My family conferenced on a screen!

My urge to pee, I will combat,
For soon there'll
Be an app for that!

Forget the attic,
Pantry, kitchen,
This bed's where I'll make my livin'!

Ah, what now?
Low battery!
I'll close shop temporarily.

Oh, wait... An outlet.
Yes! Hooray!!!
Pillow and Sheets, opens today.

DIGITAL SPACE

Is it self-preservation, an elixir to death,
That we enter this plane without second guess?
Where our hearts are all empty, our smiles a cartoon,
And our memories glossed like a fresh honeymoon.
It's all code in the end and it long will outlast
The whitening hair of each hour that's passed.
How truly unnatural, but my, is it spacious.
A grumbling stomach both starved and vexatious.
It doesn't take much to asperse it as wrong,
But perhaps we're all here 'cause it's nice to belong.

DAY THREE

Day in, day out, I'd like to shout!
I'm lost in a creative drought.
Can't sleep a wink. My pen's lost ink.
Chores mount like dishes in the sink.
My brain could use a quick jumpstart.
My only comfort's buttered tarts.
Atop the sheets that make my bed
A feathered crown clutches my head.
I watch as time droops to the floor
Becoming harder to ignore.
I drift into that realm of sleep
Escorted by a flock of sheep
And float into a grade school chair
Anxiously in my underwear.
Hold on... A thought!
I jolt awake!
At last something my mind can slake.
The drought has ended.
Pencil's sharp.
There's distant strummings of a harp.
A harp... no wait!
The thought is gone.
Next thing I know the TV's on.

Ah crud. I am distracted.
Well, an episode can't hurt.
I'll watch and then get back to writing,
Rested and alert!

Day Four ...

AVATAR

I'm window-shopping lovers
From the comfort of my bed
A curated collection
That I scroll through in my head.

I'd rather sit down face-to-face
With your uncensored hue,
For how could the display window
Capture the depths of you?

THE MAIN ATTRACTION

Come one! Come all!
You won't believe
What lurks inside my tent.
A creature born
From paradox
Who dreads the smell of rent.

I ask you now,
Don't look away,
Unsightly he may be.
Come feast your eyes
Upon the wild
Bearded ManBaby!

Adorable
Though he may seem,
I beg you, look inside.
That's where his
Immaturity
Can find no place to hide.

He's self-concerned
And symbiotic,
Full of true potential,
Yet refuses
To spend it on
Anything that substantial.

"You cannot fail
If you don't try!"
The ManBaby will wail,
While waiting on his caretaker
To stock
His feeding pail.

I caught him
Just past Neverland,
I've tried to train him since,
But lessons are all lost on him,
Not much
Seems to convince.

Whatever
Shall I do with him?
I've not the faintest clue.
I fear
If he won't get his way
He'll break into a 'tude!

Come one! Come all!
Please take a peek,
And maybe take him too!
I've caught
A Bearded ManBaby
And don't want him. Do you?

BEARDED
MANBABY
The Finest Head of Hair Ever Seen!

The SOCIETY of NOBLE OPINIONS and BELIEFS

Ugh! How droll. A commoner
Has stumbled in our midst.

Well, come along. Please don't delay.
If you wish to enlist.

A monocle's required,
Also tea and nasal spray.

You look the part. Now all that's left
Is what you have to say.

There is one rule to master
In our high society.

We groan and grumble, gossip, grouse,
But never disagree.

Should this be satisfactory,
Then welcome to our club.

If not, you best prepare to be
Habitually snubbed.

We have no time for nuance,
No stomach for subtlety.

Now are you in or out?
Don't delay with profundity.

ETIQUETTE

I led my stubborn horse down to the brook to take a sip
He bucked, whinnied, and kicked determined to give me the slip.
I stuck his face into the water, hoping he would drink,
Then something unexpected happened bound to make me think.
My horse did not appreciate the brashness of my moves
And soon I found myself beneath the might of his horse hooves.
I led my stubborn horse down to the brook to take a sip
And nearly drank the lake myself for my poor showmanship.

SCHTUM

The Captain's peace of mind
Remains my top priority
That's why I did not tell him
'Bout the growing mutiny.
I chose to keep it secret
When the hull had sprung a leak.
I plugged my nose with corks
When our rations began to reek.
The cannons were all waterlogged,
We left them all behind.
I didn't think it kind to say
The new lookout is blind.
I tried to keep our spirits up,
Meanwhile the ship went down.
I still maintain my zeal,
Although I think the Captain drowned.

GHOUL OF THE GREEK

The ghoul inside the frat house
Found it hard to scare the crowd;
He cried and wailed throughout the day,
But TV drowned him out.
He thought he'd soil their pots and pans,
But found them in the sink.
He tried to conjure up foul smells,
But added to the stink.
He sought to smash the glassware
Only to find SOLO cups.
He howled out loud at parties
Only to receive biggups.
He tried to wait for them to sleep
To finally scare them straight,
But found himself bone-weary
For they stayed up pretty late.
The ghoul inside the frat house
Couldn't seem to keep his edge,
So rather than depart
He gladly joined them as a pledge.

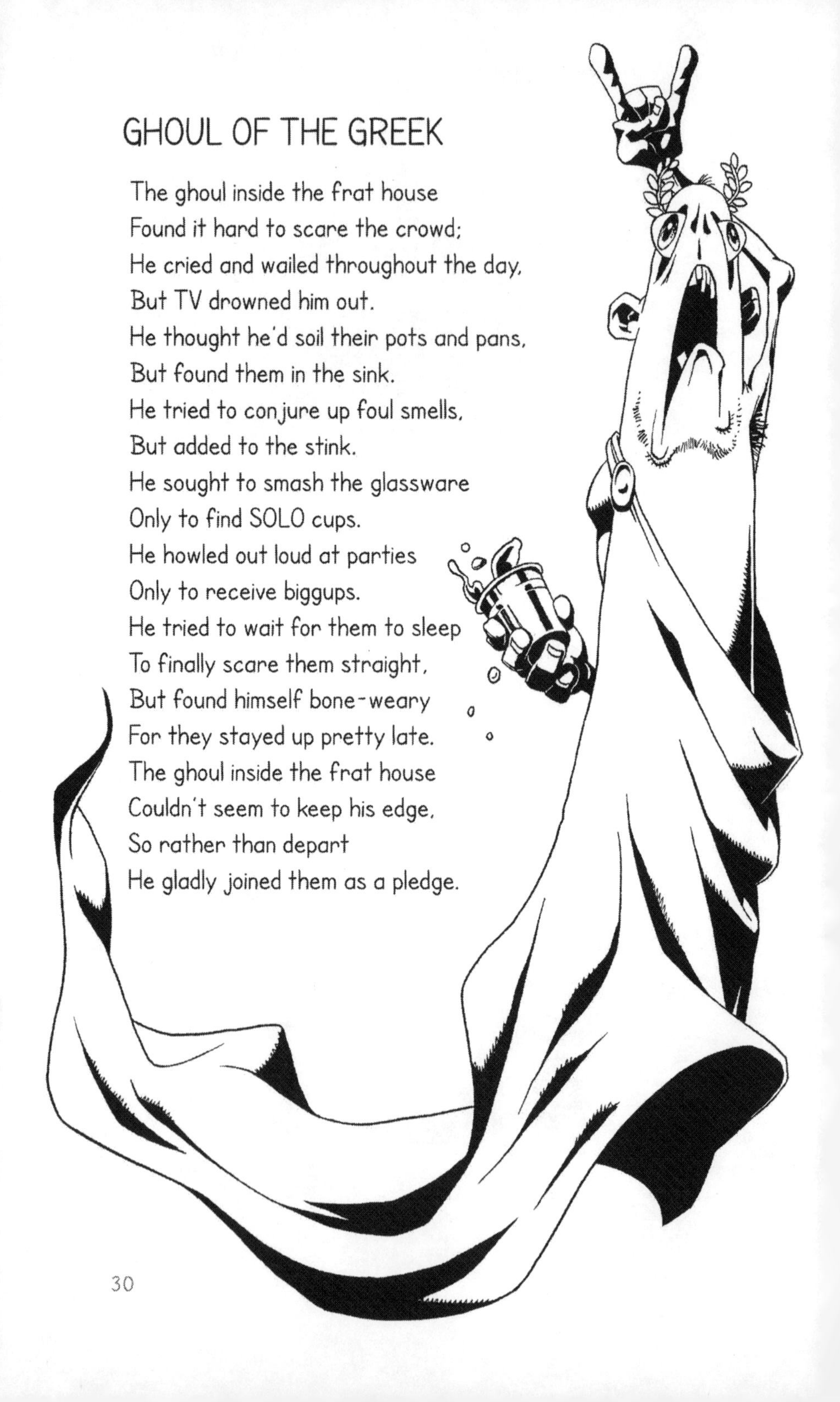

GARGOYLES

The troubled children of the night,
Apprehensive of daylight,
Avoided hours meant for bed
By dancing 'round the buried dead.
A whispered exhale from the grave
Encouraged them to misbehave
And fetch a neighbor in the ground
Whose gift for magic was profound.
Shovels, labor, brought her so
Out of the earth that lay below.
The Wicken's skeleton then spoke
A grating cacophonous croak.
She counted children, one, two, three,
Promised a wish to let her be.
The first asked to be strong and bold;
The second, never to get old.
The third wished he would be admired,
All at once, they then expired.
Statues stood, now in their place,
Each with a foul stone-crested face,
The witch returned to slumber past.
Her neighbor whispered "Peace at last."

CREATURE COMFORT

Madeline Pratt
Grew concerned with her cat
Who would sit on her bed
Ev'ry night.
Pupils like black sabers
The cat watched, and favored
When Madeline
Turned out the light.
Anxious eyes of yellow
Like toasted marshmallows
Watched Madeline
Drift off to sleep,
And that's when the cat,
For the warmth of its fat,
Would sleep on her head
With delight.

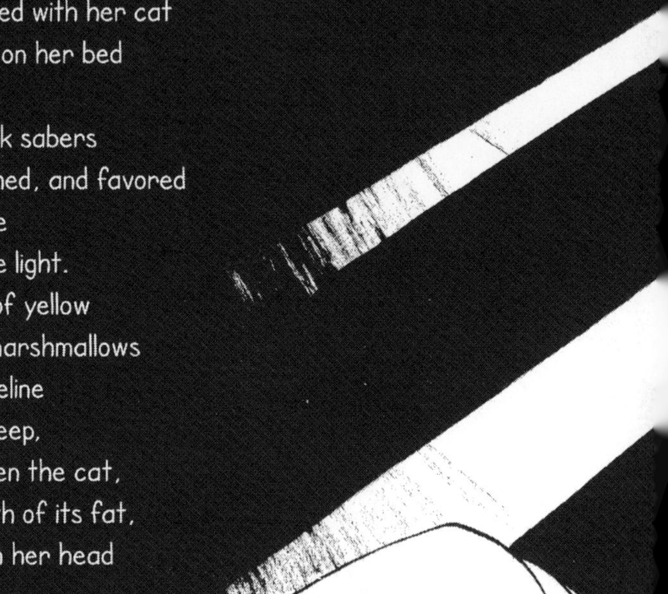

FIREFLY

How do the ants and spiders see the brilliant firefly?
With envy do they observe ev'ry twinkle in the sky?
Do they wonder why their bottoms fail to light up just the same?
Do they watch children give chase instead of simply run away?
For their sake, I sure hope they don't,
Some people do that plenty:
They see beautiful things
And somehow only feel more empty.

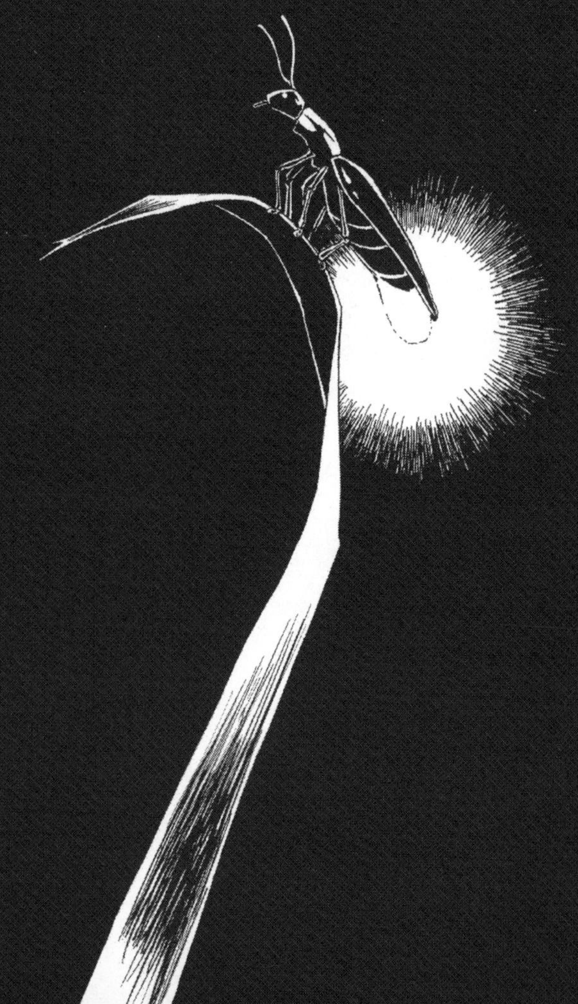

THE GOOZLEBOOG

All right, be quiet. Here he is
My friend the Goozleboog.
He's standing by my record player
Relishing a fugue.

Be sure to keep your voice low
Please do not upset my friend.
The music's only started
And the Boog hates when it ends.

Don't make a peep or interrupt,
He's dancing to the tune.
He's shuffling his massive paws
Enticed by the bassoon.

Shh! Speak softer. What was that?
You don't believe he's real?
How could I fake an eight-foot dog-like
Monster so surreal?

WAIT! DO NOT TOUCH THAT LIGHT SWITCH
FOR HE DOESN'T LIKE FLUORESCENTS.
THE BRIGHTNESS MAKES HIM CRANKY -
NEED I REPEAT MY LAST SENTENCE?

I told you not to, but you did,
And now he's trashed my room.

I never should have shared
With such a skeptical buffoon.

RHYME BOX

My Rhyme-Box is broken and now I am sad,
I wrote a new poem, which came out quite - poor.

There has to be a loose knob or a screw!
I fear that I've bitten off too much to - chomp.

What remedy will fix this mess?
I fear I'll buckle under - strain.

So many pages left to go.
Without rhymes they're just tales of -
Disparate sad things, I guess?

KNOWLEDGE

Becky the bookworm
Filled up her head
With ev'ry book
That could ever be read.

"Encyclopedic!"
The crowd called her wit,
But Becky just sat
Wond'ring how she'd apply it?

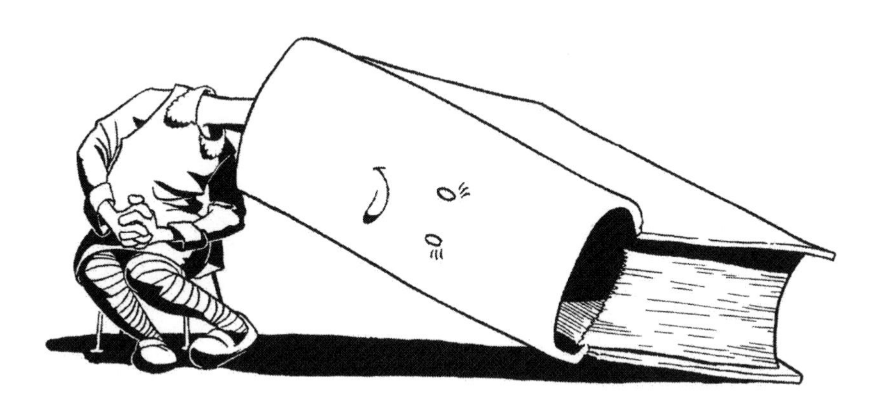

HIGH HEELS

Moldable like clay,
The youthful pupil did his tasks,
Fulfilling each request
His senior officemates would ask.

One day he met a higher-up
With shoes unseen before.
Instead of heels or flats
She wore two interns on the floor.

On hands and knees they held her up
And took her ev'ry step.
She wore them through the building
Even past the HR rep.

When asked about her fashion choice
She said to get ahead
You sport footwear like hers
Or will become a pair instead.

The pupil tried a set
And so began his worst week yet,
For ev'ry step he made
Was by another person's sweat.

A week was long enough,
He congregated all the shoes,
And urged them to walk on their own
So they could earn their dues.

At least, I wish that's what he'd did,
His footwork remained tense.
Regrettably, a year of steps
Came at others' expense.

The pupil learned a lesson
Without guardian or guide
That others shouldn't kneel
So that you can hit your stride.

THE KNIGHTS OF NEVERMORE

With swords and spears they strut about:
The Knights of Nevermore!
Uprooting evil in the land
They kept a keen eye for.

And when the day was good and won
They didn't celebrate.
They plainly took up arms elsewhere
Hell-bent to extricate.

They charged through kingdoms,
Stalked the serfs, relaxed among the boar,
And all the while declared
That evil would be nevermore!

Then finally, the day arrived,
The sinful had been smothered,
But did the Knights rest easy?
No, they turned on one another.

TOY HORSE

Is a toy horse
A horse?
A horse?
Well, of course!
Of course!
Of course!
But I wouldn't expect it
To carry the weight
Of a horse.
A horse.
A horse.

PRELUDE

Between the kingdom of Keep-It-Down,
Where racket incurs the wrath of frowns,
And the western stronghold of Stuff-Your-Ears,
Where few abide what they'd rather not hear,
Rests the Palace of Pretty Preludes,
Where unprefaced dialogue inspires 'tudes.
Chatterbox babblers all take a chance
If they don't first engage in a song and dance:
A melodic and mandated qualifier
Before one speaks, lest they promptly retire.
Each year the magistrate edits the words
And updates the steps to what they would prefer.
The tune becomes longer, the moves more complex;
Exchanges grow harder for Palace subjects.
Those with complaints are all seen as curmudgeons
And swiftly displaced to the Palace's dungeons.
Singing and dancing goes on all day long,
While the villagers struggle to move things along.
The onlooking kingdoms all marvel "What fun,"
But the prelude gums up getting anything done.

THE PLASTIC PRINCESS

As I was fishing on the beach
Along the sandy shore,
I saw a sight I won't forget
My eyes could not ignore.
A princess laced in plastic
Rode two turtles through the sea
Inside a milk jug carriage.
This was not hyperbole!
She'd toilet rolls curled in her hair,
A frilly paper crown,
And reins of floss she'd whip and toss
To steer her creatures 'round.
She charged in my direction,
And it became clear to me,
The plastic from my sandwich bag
Had fallen in the sea.
Before I could react
She cuffed me with some six-pack rings,
I watched her take her litter stick
And pluck my plastic things.
She told me she would let me go,
But warned of her pursuit,
To capture anyone who dared
To litter or pollute.
Then off she went back to the sea,
I sat wide-eyed and idle,
And now you know exactly why
I'd rather just recycle.

OLD FRIEND

I thought it would take TNT,
The clap of wild thunder,
But all it took was silence
To dispatch this ship asunder.

THE ROAD

Sonny couldn't help but run
From each and ev'ry stare,
From ev'ry pair of pretty eyes
That shook him with despair;

From ev'ry pair of glossy lips
That made him look away,
He fashioned his own ruse
So he would never have to stay.

He sprinted down the road,
Which he'd begun to call his home,
And realized too late
That he was running all alone.

He stopped to curse the very street
That nurtured him before
And wished another pair of eyes
Would unnerve him once more.

SHADOWBOXING

Gloves up
Head down
I've stepped into another round.

Bell rings
Three chimes
I try to read between the lines.

Check hook
Set. Thrown.
Contending, but I'm all alone.

Trial horse
On the ropes
Rebuttals, comebacks, hurtful jokes.

Eight count
Short breath
Why is it that I'm so obsessed?

Shoulder roll
Quick slip
Stressing out. Please get a grip.

Footwork
Underdog.
Live presently or parry fog.

FOGHEAD

Through the misty mornings
Of cloudy eyes
Foghead walks with his disguise:
A veil of smoke
To shield his face
From what he'd rather not embrace.

His hazy habits multiply
Like dreary rabbits
With each sigh;
A whipped-cream armor
Ersatz transcendent,
On which he's become dependent.

But the clouds
May break away
In favor of a brighter day,
For Foghead,
First afraid to yelp,
Summoned the strength
To ask for help.

THE
DARKEST
CORNER

ACCOUNTABILITY

That writhing in your gut
That comes with doing something wrong
Indulges in the thought
That punishment must be prolonged.
Fear takes ahold of all your strings,
Becomes the puppeteer,
And whispers plans of an escape
If you just let it steer.
I'm warning you right now
That should you let fear take control,
Autonomy becomes
An inward struggle to cajole.
However, should you snip the strings
And act responsibly,
While fear may hang around
You will be absolutely free.

FINN

On his first day at school
Billy teased shark-boy Finn.
Billy vanished at recess.
No one teased Finn again.

DAREWOLVES

There are Starewolves, Contrarewolves, and howling Despairwolves,
Impairwolves and Scarewolves, compassionate Carewolves,
But you best be careful should you meet a Darewolf!
They're tough to impress and are often unfair wolves.

They like to talk big and their bark's truly feral.
They steer others straight into oncoming peril.
And should you succeed overcoming their test,
They'll take all the credit for you at your best.

Should you spot a Darewolf,
Feel free, test your might,
But all I have found
Is that they simply bite.

NOSTALGIA

One single drop is all you need
To float into that space
Where ev'rything felt right
And not a detail out of place.
An ephemeral experience
To help you get away
From all the trials and tribulations
Of your present day.
A word of warning, should you dare
To have more than your fill,
The past may not be as inviting
On your second spill.
The mind's an awf'lly tricky maze
Concealed in memory's fog,
And while you wrestle days gone by
The present moves along.

FROM THE BOWELS OF MY ART

For this remake the part of Heart
Will be played by the Brain.
The story's been repackaged
And resold to you again.

The algorithmic ant farm
Thought they'd rescue your deposit
Inside the discontented clutches
Of your purse or wallet.

Instead of risk n' adventure,
There's nostalgia and appeal,
That condescends with tired bits
Like the banana peel.

At best, there's more of what you like,
At worst, more disappointment.
Meanwhile, daring new tales
Continue filing for unemployment.

The cow's been milked to powdered mix,
The dead horse kicked alive
By stories you once saw and loved,
Now you just roll your eyes.

They're not all bad, don't get me wrong,
But this for me is true,
I'd rather be let down by something
That at least was new.

UNBEATABLE

Strangers from Mars
Filled with wicked intent
Turned tail and went home so that they could repent.

A scientist
Sworn to serve vengeance and doom
Had his plot swiftly foiled and license deplumed.

No matter the size
Of the threat that emerged
Two heroes made sure that all evil was purged.

Unbeatable Betty
Unbeatable Bill
Could seldom be matched in their power or skill.

They were fearless and flawless,
They shunned fear and doubt,
Weakness was something they both lived without.

Their deeds were substantial,
It's hardly debatable.
Truthfully though, neither was that relatable.

B
B

THE S.C.C.

We're the Superhero Cleanup Crew.
We pick up once the day is through.
We sweep the sidewalks, pave the street,
Repair road signs and scrap concrete.
Despite frequent catastrophe,
We carry on most affably.
While people in the city say
They'd rather no one save the day.

BRUISES

Roughneck Nick
Had a bone to pick
With the rogues that sat in his bar.

He showed off his bruises,
Quotidian abuses,
He claimed would outclass any scar.

Crooked-Back Craig,
Whose ears had been plagued
By Roughneck's bawling defiance,

Had been kicked in the rear,
Also tortured for years
By a clamorous kitchen appliance.

He chuckled at Nick
For believing too quick
In the glory of flesh freshly cankered

When Miscreant Mary,
With knuckles quite hairy,
Just laughed as she guzzled her tankard.

Neither Craig nor Nick
Had been hit with a brick,
A luxury Mary knew twice,

But Vicky the Vandal,
Burnt twice by a candle,
Followed suit with her own tale of vice.

Then Steven the Scoundrel,
Tinsel-Tooth Tess,
And Nefarious Nibbled-Ear Neal

All stood up to brag
'Bout misfortunes they'd had,
And continued one-upping with zeal.

From comparison's sprout,
A fight blossomed out
Over every scratch, wound, and stitch.

Such a shame pain's degrees
Were misused for prestige
When they make for a much better bridge.

WHY SPY

It cannot be fun to seek work as a spy
For how could you discern the truth from a lie?
Are you keenly suspicious of each passerby?
Can you trust a new neighbor who gifts you a pie?
Is your mother your mom or a paid private eye?
Do you read into words for what they may imply?
Are your letters containing invisible dye?
Is your shoe a grenade? Does garrote line your tie?
No, it cannot be fun to seek work as a spy.
So tell me then, why do I?

MISFORTUNE MANAGEMENT

Do inheritance squabbles make you nervous?
Misfortune Management at your service.
Noisy neighbors spoiling your sleep?
Soon you'll hardly hear a peep.
Bothered by a clingy ex?
Dress your best to pay respects.
Spousal issues in the house?
We'll be quiet as a mouse.
Awkward elders causing stares?
Hopefully they're good with stairs.
Anything you wish would cease
We guarantee to put at ease.
Come again? You wish to leave?
Well, consultation isn't free.
You cannot simply walk away.
I'm sorry, but you'll have to pay.

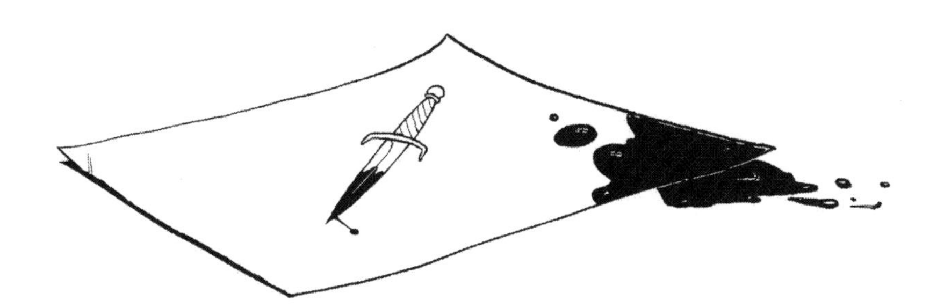

STALLIN'

He oppressed out in the West,
She crushed dissent out East.
Meanwhile the land that lay between them
Ripened to be fleeced.

Each argued for their claim,
They spat out insults filled with phlegm,
But neither could deny
The love that tyrannized within.

A union quickly formed,
A pact malevolent and cruel,
Together they would scourge the Earth
With mis'ry as their fuel.

Now, just what is the moral here,
This tale of woe does send?
Quite simply put, that true love
Need not have a happy end.

THE LOVE CODE

There's a secret combination,
A consortium of words,
That uttered at a precise moment
Yield something absurd.
The listener will find themselves
Immobilized with love,
They'll look at you, the speaker,
As someone sent from above.
To ev'ryone who thought me silly,
Told me just say "Hi,"
I've proven that there is in fact
A right place and right time.
I've written down a foolproof plan,
I've crunched the numbers twice,
Now all I need's a test subject
And we'll find paradise!

WAX PROMISES

This thing that we built
On paraffin trust
Displays all the signs of romance,
But turn up the heat
And it's easy to see
That our love never stood a chance.

ALL THE DATA ALL THE TIME

I wake to an electric hum
That rings beside my bed,
Have each step counted when I'm up
And wherever I tread.
My wrist sends me a notice
About items small or dire,
While sleeping tools
All feed off of my house with lengthy wire.
Seated, I consult a window
Open to the world.
Plastic bugs dig in my ears
'Til properly unfurled.
A neon puck keeps listen
Should I dare to say a peep.
Content, chats, and advertisements
Flood my eyes in heap.
Connection is convenient,
But it's harder ev'ry day
To focus on the bright side
When you cannot turn away.

DANGEROUSLY CHEESY

The cat's been declawed;
The dog stuck outside.
The Mouse is in charge,
Now the house is cockeyed.

The parents and kids
Are all forced to make cheese
For their new rodent ruler
They live to appease.

The Mouse did away
With the art in their halls
And placed cheddar portraits
All over their walls.

He raided their screening room,
Swiped the shelves clean,
For DVDs he would now
Privately screen.

The Mouse only shows
What the Mouse likes to see,
While the fam'ly conforms
To his cheesy decrees.

They say mole hills make mountains,
But who would have guessed
That a sinkhole could spring
From the nest of a pest?

PETE & REPEAT

If I say it out loud,
If I say it once more,
Does that make what I say
More correct than before?
If I say it until
The whole world distorts,
'Til logic and reason
Abandon retorts,
Then who am I helping,
Except perhaps me?
To assuage my discomfort
With reality.
No, I can't welcome doubt
So, I'll say it once more,
And this time I will say it
Louder than before!

IF I SAY IT OUT LOUD ...

IF TOMORROW NEVER COMES

A million things I'd like to say
If I should make it through the day.
A million things all left unsaid
That shame has jangled in my head.
A million ways to tell you
What you really mean to me.
A million ways to act on
What our life could really be.
The waves of fear recede
And in the comfort of content,
There sit a million things
All left entirely unsaid.

THE WELL

On the edge of oblivion
An old water well.
Some call it Heaven
To others it's Hell.
Its depth is immeasurable
Though many still try
Some ponder its contents,
While others stay shy.

All have to look down
There is no exception.
Staring back up:
A dim rippled complexion.
A mirror to
All of your inward desires
Declared or dismissed
On your funeral pyre.

What did you see
In the old water well?
Was it from Heaven
Or possibly Hell?
Will it compel you
To live gracefully?
Or will you go mad
From the horror you see?

DESTINY

Trixy the Terrible
Set up traps
So alone her witchcraft could thrive.

Inside her hovel
She kept a prize
For any who found her alive.

Seated in her rocking chair,
She waited
Anxiously.

Until the day
She passed away
Unnoticed tragic'ly.

While people sing
About the knights
Who searched for her and fell,

The rest of us
Just sing about
The traps she set too well.

THE PALE HORSE

Clip-clop clip-clop
The pale horse treads
With pestilence
In tow.
The grass beneath
Each hoof
Desaturates
To pale yellow.

Clip-clop clip-clop
A haunting whinny
Whistles
Through the trees.
Cathedral bells
With muted knells
All crumble
To debris.

Clip-clop clip-clop
The end is near
The restless all
Talk shop,
But not a deed,
Nor word, nor creed
Can stop
Clip-clop clip-clop ...

YELLOW SKY

As each silo exhaled, a defense siren wailed
Beneath the Yellow Sky.

Children huddled 'neath desks filled with thoughts so grotesque
Beneath the Yellow Sky.

The suits and cigars braced in bunkers and bars
Beneath the Yellow Sky.

Some clung all alone
To their laptops or phones
Beneath the Yellow Sky.

Others clung
To their
Brothers,
Dads,
Sisters,
Or mothers,
Beneath
The
Yellow Sky.

With
The click of
A key
All we knew
Ceased
To be
Beneath the Yellow Sky.

Fire fed fire
The hatred grew higher
Destruction was born
Out of bitter desire
The last stone was cast
And the rubble amassed
The world that we knew
Was snuffed out
In a blast.
Would you let it all burn
Just to say it's my turn?
LOST
Have you seen my stuffed bear
With the blue button eye?
I'm afraid that he's lost
And I worry he'll cry.
I'll be King of the ash!
I'll be Queen of the soot!
I'll rebuild in my image
What was trampled by foot!
"I want to be happy,"
But what does that mean?
I worry I'll flounder
In cracks and betweens
What I'd give for just one day in traffic.
Would you answer with sticks?
Would you answer with stones?
Would you rather I wind up disgraced
And alone?
What happened to you
And your will to forgive?
Do I not share your right to live?
Hope was the tonic
To despair's disease.
What are we without it?
Could you tell me please?

I gazed in the void of endless potential
Discovering something private and substantial.
Now I am off 'til the day that I die
With a quest I selected and can't help but try.
What is the burden you're willing to bear
To untether yourself from the clutch
of despair?
Errands:
- Grocery store for Eggs and Milk
- Art supplies and decorative Silk
The nihilist thought, "I don't care to rhyme ...
But I guess I could try it, just this one time."
There are people with pins,
Ornate crested flats,
And people who wear
Tall funny-shaped hats.
What fools to think
That they've figured it out,
And how quickly they need help
From your bank account.
'bout ear to ear?
Okay, we don't see ear to ear,
But how 'bout nose to nose?
My heart beats as yours,
So then why must we fight?
Instead take my hand
And let's conquer the night.
- Unknown

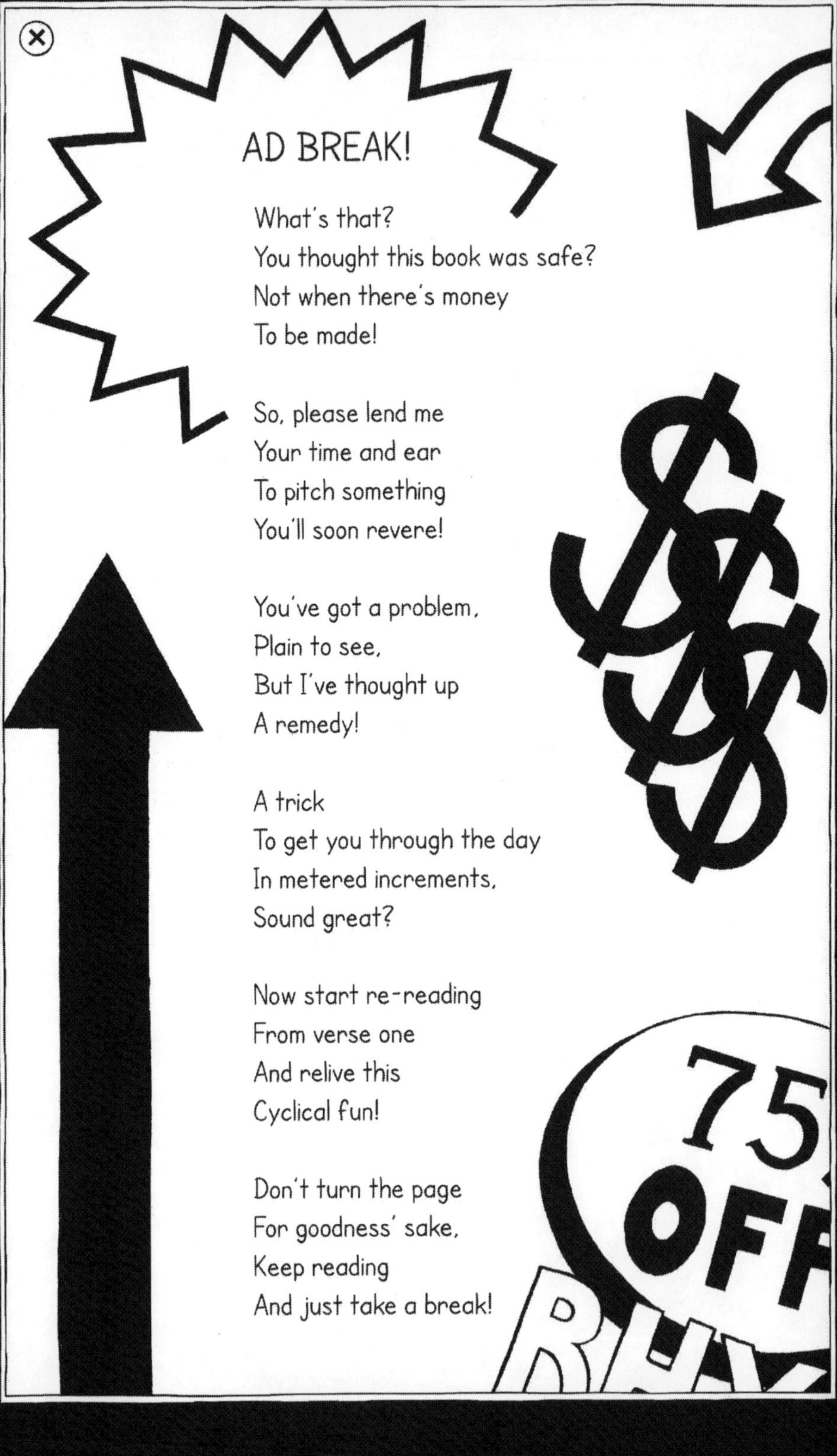

AD BREAK!

What's that?
You thought this book was safe?
Not when there's money
To be made!

So, please lend me
Your time and ear
To pitch something
You'll soon revere!

You've got a problem,
Plain to see,
But I've thought up
A remedy!

A trick
To get you through the day
In metered increments,
Sound great?

Now start re-reading
From verse one
And relive this
Cyclical fun!

Don't turn the page
For goodness' sake,
Keep reading
And just take a break!

RINGMASTER

Hello, old friend. It's me again
The Sachem of Suspense!
The Umpire of Uncertainty!
The Head of Hesitance!
I knew that we would reconvene,
We would, we will, we have.
Your view of me's myopic
So I came to share my half.

It's true, the rumors that you've heard,
I'll gobble up your dreams,
I'll build an atmosphere
Where you distrust trying new things.
Before you zip my lips however,
Please consider this,
Perhaps our colloquy's too gloomy
To respect my gifts.

The Captain of Confusion
Has been carved on my marquee,
But did you know
I'm Handyman to your discovery?
I'll help you keep an open mind
Improve your analytics.
Allow dissent, where "Us v. Them"
Would demonize your critics.

Investigate the status quo;
Investigate your fears;
I'll pave the way to revelation
In your new frontier.
How long we speak and what we say
Will make us foe or friend.
I'll walk beside you ev'ry step,
On that you can depend.

And so, dear friend, the case I make,
Depends how I'm employed,
I am both skepticism
And paralytic schadenfreude.
How we proceed is up to you,
I'll be there either way,
The circus always stays in town,
What will be on display?

I FEEL THEREFORE IT IS

The world had a compassion problem:
Booked a serviceman
Who set to work with good intent,
But a misguided plan.
Inside his kit was forced compliance,
Ostracism, shame,
Finger-pointing, arrogance,
Guilt, and laying blame.
The problem lingers still
And seems to worsen with these tactics,
For while the world spins on
Fear has its finger on the axis.

HORIZON

TREASURE

There's a parrot seated on my shoulder.
Ev'ry year he's growing older.

"Squack," he says. "Today the day?"
"There's still too much to do," I say.

He flies abroad, but ev'ry morning
Probes me with the same forewarning.

Who knows when the day will come
He'll tire of our one-on-one.

Until he does, I'll take delight
In his frustration with my slight.

I love to keep the bird at bay
And sail that rich auspicious fray.

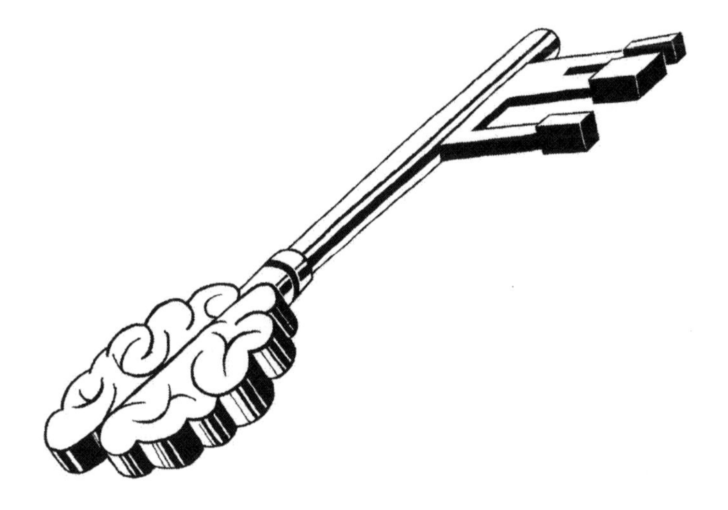

LAUGHTER

There is no sweeter sound on Earth,
Nor in this galaxy.
No fresher air I fight to breath
As spontaneously.
No potion quite as piquant
When I'm painted blue with strife.
No bridge as wide or stable
For so many walks of life.
No sight as stunning as a pair
Of shoulders shuddering.
No smell quite like a microphone
Tainted from sputtering.
No simple act as personal
Nor filled with honesty.
Forever I'm your servant.
Thanks for all you've given me.

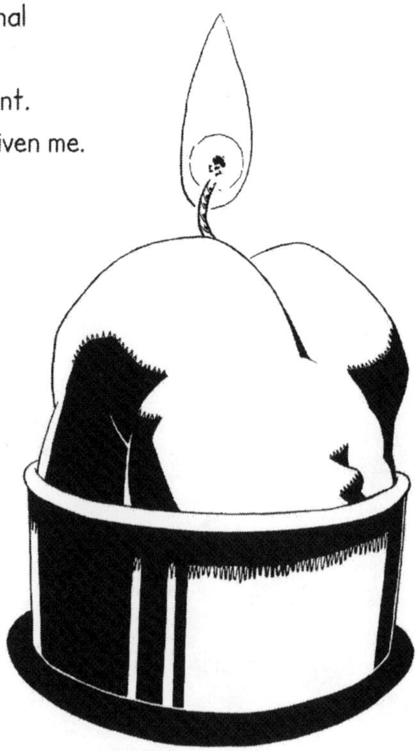

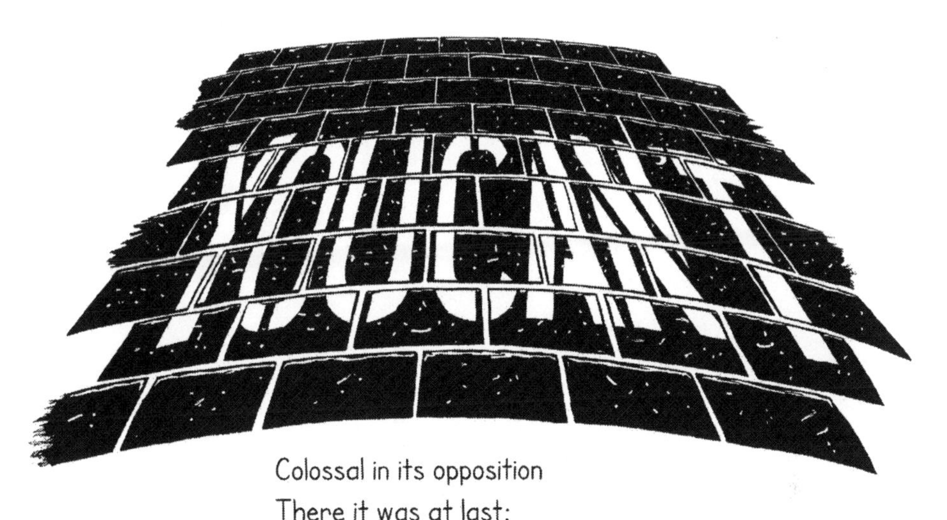

Colossal in its opposition
There it was at last:
The wall which boldly said "You Can't"
His father had forecast.
It stood without an envoy
Daring all enthusiasts
To place their hands upon its face
And push until they quit.
Many tried, many do,
Many walk away.
The traveler, however,
Knew deep down he had to stay.
His arms were weak, his feet were tired,
But he did not care.
He was precisely in that spot
To which none could compare.
And so he pushes on the wall
Knowing it won't budge,
Knowing that the wall will stand
Long after this poor drudge.
Still knowing this, he doesn't stop,
Relentless as a fool,
He learned to love the push
And now "You Can't" has become fuel.

SOME GOOD CRAP

"Can you believe this crap?"
Said a dung beetle to its brother.
"You're telling me! I think I'll save some
For our pops and mother!"

Ah, to be a dung beetle.
How could life get you down
When crappy living is the best
There is to go around?

BRUSH YOUR TEETH

Hazel the nut
Sat her butt in a rut
Then she shoveled
The ground with her hands.
She'd wake up an oak
If the rain soaked her cloak
Made from all of
The scooped up sand.

A small effort each day
Can purvey your headway
If you're willing
To put in the time.
Just like Hazel the nut
Who strut out of her rut
As a tree
That had mastered the climb.

A REGULAR

I'm not a force of nature.
I'm a human just like you.
An average Joe who eats too much
And overthinks things too.
I wake up in the morning
Quite compelled to sleep some more.
I hide the crumbs I spill
Beneath the rug upon my floor.
There's plenty left to work on
And I'm quite compelled to try,
But don't ever mistake me for
An omnipotent guy.

THE MILKY WAY

The moon is made of cheese,
The man atop it's lactose-free.
He pondered what the sun was like
Beneath a Gouda tree.
He grabbed his Chhurpi tools
And built a rocket made of Brie,
Then took off past the stars
Expelling Provolone debris.
Now, did he make it to the sun?
My mother didn't say,
But Ms. Welsh, she told me
That's how he formed our Milky Way.

SUBURBAN

I dug my cleats into the gravel,
Swung with all my might.
My baseball flew into the sky
And vanished out of sight.

A booming crash sprang from the garden
Just beyond the fence.
The neighbor cursed obscenities
Demanding recompense.

The players scattered, all but me,
A frozen front yard gnome
Fixated on the broken window
In my neighbor's home.

Repair men came, my mother yelled,
The summer turned to fall,
And ev'ry time I'd walk the block
I heard my stray fly ball.

College pulled me from the 'burbs,
But winter brought me back,
That's when I learned our next door neighbor
Left the cul-de-sac.

Their house lay vacant
Buried in the weight of winter's quilt,
Abandoned without owners
Left to wither, waste, and wilt.

I stepped onto the lawn
Before the window I knew well
And still could hear the cracking glass
Succeeded by a yell.

I've moved across the country,
Yet still dream about that day,
One summer in my neighborhood
Where part of me still plays.

MUSIC

With the clap of copper cymbals
I'm compelled to sing your name,
Conducted by acoustics
Echoing inside my brain.
A thumping bass drum slaps on beat
Buried beneath my breast.
An orchestra of organs
Seat themselves to play the rest.
I went for weeks without a song,
A theater without sound,
Your footsteps are my metronome
Now music's all around!

THE UNKNOWN

What is that terrifying shape
That looms out in the dark?
What horrid features will my own
Imagination spark?
What threat does it conceal
Within its cruel clandestine form?
And why am I convinced
That it intends to do me harm?

THE BUNKER

Worry-Wart Warren came up with a scheme
To assemble a bunker both safe and pristine.
A place where discomfort would not be allowed,
And build it he did to keep everyone out.
Confined all alone to his new metal den
He conversed with the echoes resounding within,
And laugh how he did, at their ev'ry remark,
For soundness of mind was his brand-new benchmark.
His bunker supplies soon began to run out,
So he rejoined a world filled with questions and doubt,
Where he shuddered and winced at a place now so foreign,
Then swiftly retreated for all felt abhorrent.
Now Worry Wart-Warren just sits in his base,
While the world outside keeps its usual pace.
He watches the change of each season's decline
From a hole in the fort of his own design.

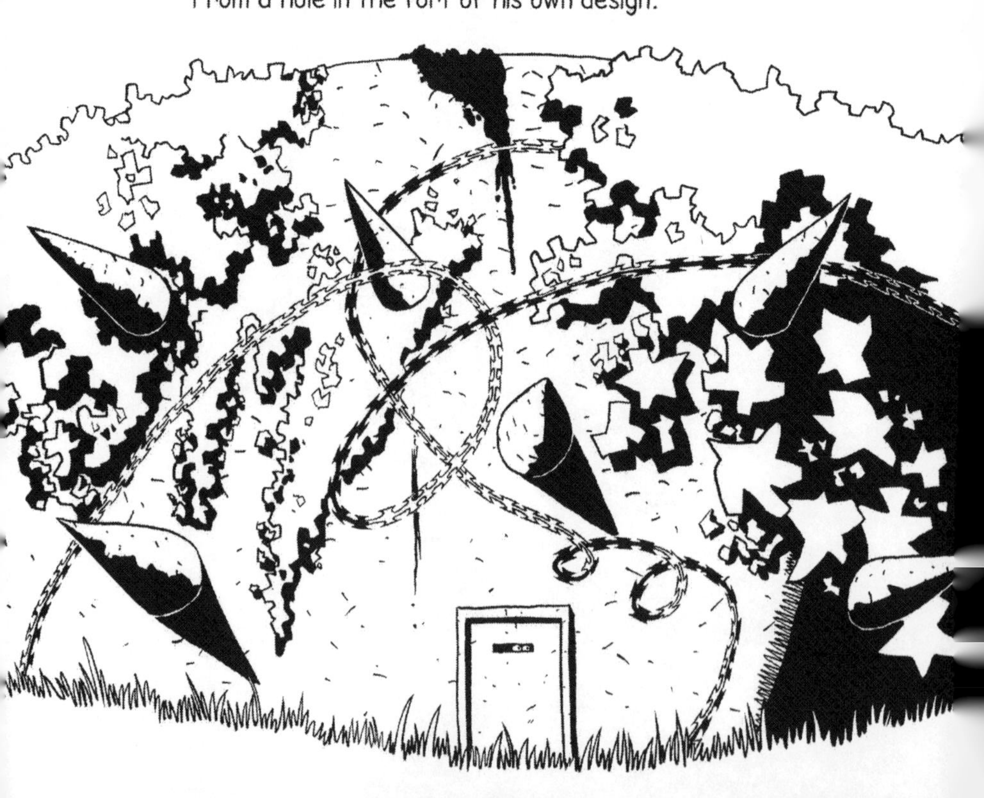

OF SCALES AND STEEL

Although we wield
Both sword and shield
It's not a guarantee
That we're the knight
Noble and bright
Composed of bravery.

The making of
A gentle dove
Dwells in our humble nature,
So too the ire
That breathes fire
And would scorch our neighbor.

ROBUST

If I could gather all your pain
And hold it in my hands
To spare your cheek the blemishes
From each teardrop that lands,
I'd feel just like a bodyguard
And shield you from what's scary,
But then how would you learn
This ache is only temporary?

OF WENDY AND THE WOLF

Wendy walked into the woods
Despite her mother's warning,
Swallowed by the jagged branches
Leafless and in mourning.
She hummed to keep her spirits high,
But couldn't shake the notion
That something in the brush
Observed her with lustful devotion.

Suddenly, her skin went white,
A drooling Wolf appeared,
It snarled with a crooked grin
That stretched from ear to ear.
The creature licked its lips
While Wendy chose which way to flee,
A mighty roar startled the pair
Emerging violently.

The Woman of the Woods,
Who bore a steel axe in her hand,
Carved a path between the two
And bravely took a stand.
The Woman's arms had suffered
Bruises, bite marks, wounds and scars.
The beast retreated angrily,
Its eyes corrupted stars.

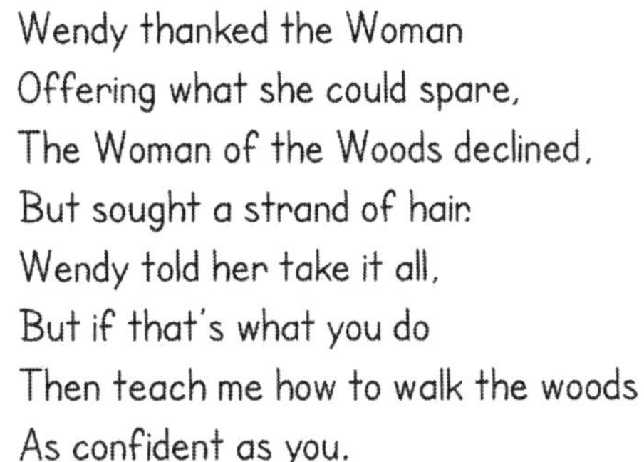

Wendy thanked the Woman
Offering what she could spare,
The Woman of the Woods declined,
But sought a strand of hair.
Wendy told her take it all,
But if that's what you do
Then teach me how to walk the woods
As confident as you.

Within the tangled woods
A cabin blossomed comfortably,
Where future generations
Flourished in prosperity.
Inside a little girl
Wears her mother's souvenir,
A wolf-tooth necklace to remind her
She can tame her fear.

WOLF

It sounds quite absurd,
But what good is the word
If you call ev'rything a "Wolf?"

For critters walking on all fours
Won't understand
What lies in store

When horses, zebras,
Even cows,
Are seen as predators somehow.

Squirrels and rabbits with gray fur,
Had better get some dye
For sure.

The indoor cats with pointed ears
Will find it hard
To keep careers,

Meanwhile the pack
Will disappear,
Blending into a thick veneer

Where wolves and corgis,
Each that howl,
Are scrutinized for matching jowls.

A threat's at risk
Of growing stale
If all too commonly availed.

How will we know the danger's real
If all alarms
Prompt equal zeal?

MORT

Death brought his son to work one day
To learn the family trade.
Mort grabbed his training scythe,
But frankly felt a bit dismayed.
His father wanted someone fierce
To reap the souls that passed,
While Mort enjoyed the flowers
That each tombstone had amassed.

They went across the globe
Collecting souls of ev'ry kind.
Death showed him all his tricks,
But Mort had something else in mind.
He wandered in the garden
While Death stalked their victim's house,
And rearranged the flowers
For the next of kin or spouse.

Death claimed the one they came for
To the tears of the bereaved,
Mort built a floral pattern
To honor the one she grieved.
When Death observed her solace
In the garden Mort had groomed,
He welcomed Mort's vocation
With a shack to be festooned.

At e'vry wake and funeral,
Amidst a dull background,
Are flowers to console
The loss of those who aren't around.
Some come from fam'ly, some from friends,
Some from the realm of souls,
Where Mort the florist builds a bouquet
For whom the bell tolls.

SHADES

Rosy Red or Ocean Blue?
Which pair of shades
Will you look through?

Cat Eyes, Brow Bar, Rounds or Squares?
Don't settle
For one measly pair.

Specs may compliment your features,
Midst the crowd
Of night-light creatures,

But shade from the glowing masses
Starts with your
Unique sunglasses.

RADIOACTIVE

The Radioactive Woman lived alone in Wasteland Park
Consigned to a polluted place the town left in the dark.
Her body radiated a peculiar green glow
That terrified the mothers who despised her green borough.
They warned the town that she was toxic, poisoning the air,
And put up signs around her home so others would beware.
Despite the slander, curses, labels, she remained unfazed,
And greeted each bystander with a wave and smiling face.
Regardless of her moniker, she knew who was inside,
And wouldn't let their words wound what she didn't have to hide.
The untold perk of being called a hazard to all else
Is that she'd prove them wrong by merely acting like herself.

X-RAY VISION

It's funny how with just one look
There's so much you can see:
Some worn out shoes, a fraying collar
Conduct that's carefree.

A cul-de-sac that offered kids
A place where they could play,
A dog who slept up on your bed
To scare the ghosts away.

A summer spent with grandma
Where she taught you how to draw,
And days you saw her speechless
In the clutch of cancer's maw.

A home that had collapsed
Into a fight around your fate,
And arguments you couldn't voice
Behind the dinner plate.

A school with many faces
Where you struggled to feel buoyant,
Assumptions made behind your back
Because you were flamboyant.

A few nights spent each week
Atop a bed too small for three,
While noises from your neighbors
Were drowned out by the TV.

A little sister
Whom you made up stories for each night,
While just outside, her custody
Was grounds for a new fight.

A stage where you could let out
All the pain inside your breast,
An opportunity
Within a concrete jungle's nest.

A multitude of stories
Which you could find anywhere
And ev'ry single one
Available from just a stare.

ON TOP OF A GREAT GREEN GIANT

In the cradle of nature's arm
I built my house up on a hill.
The birds and bugs all gathered 'round
To watch me from my window sill.

Alone in bed, I prepared to sleep,
When the earth shook with defiance.
I ran outside and discovered I'd built
My home on a great green giant!

The creature eyed me curiously
Then it let out a powerful yawn,
Which knocked me off my feet
And sent waves rippling through the lawn.

I crawled back in my house,
Upset that I'd made a mistake,
In building on an unseen neighbor
Bound to be a headache.

At night it picked through my garbage
Gathering compost for its jaws.
Each morning I woke with a tremor
As the creature stretched its paws.

It shook my wind chimes for its amusement,
Giggled whenever I mowed.
My patience was worn paper-thin,
My temper doomed to explode!

On a stormy day, I packed my car;
The creature watched me fume.
Then all of a sudden, a bone-chilling bolt
Surprised us with a BOOM!

A damaged oakwood, sprung by lightning,
Fell intended for me.
I covered both my eyes
For my demise was guaranteed.

Raindrops drummed atop the grass.
The wind whipped angrily.
Surprised, I opened both my eyes;
The creature had caught the tree.

It dropped the log and scooped me up
To shield me from the gales
That tore my home from gables
Down to the foundation's nails.

At last, the tempest settled,
Then the creature set me free.
I stepped back on the lawn
To devastation and debris.

With nothing left, I groaned a sigh,
Collapsing to my knees,
Disrupted by a familiar clack
That rustled in the breeze.

My chimes hung from a sheet of bark
Ripped from the fallen tree
That the creature held aloft
Just like a verdant canopy.

The creature I'd believed
To be a nuisance to my peace
Not only saved my life,
But made a shelter for my ease.

I tapped the wooden chimes,
Which clapped a melody for us.
The creature smiled wider
Than a hippopotamus.

At once, I knew how to repay
My neighbor I'd dismissed,
I'd build a home, not just for me,
Where we could co-exist.

In the cradle of nature's arm
I live atop a great green giant,
A hearty helpful heap of earth
That once seemed noncompliant.

Alone in bed, I drift asleep
To a harmonious rap,
The sound of wind chimes hung up
For a great green giant to tap.

GRIOT

Wandering through villages
With a satchel full of seeds,
She planted one for any
Who would share a song or mead.
She slept beneath the midnight moon
In farmers' bales of hay,
Communed with poets in the streets
Performing for their pay.
Hiking through the Grueling Gulch
She climbed among the giants.
She navigated violent waves
Aboard with drunken pirates.
She sauntered through the desert,
Haboobs hurling sand and stone,
But never lingered long enough
To make a place her home.
The Griot wandered East to West
Until she went unseen,
But left behind a trail of stories
Sowed in leaves of green.

CARTOGRAPHERS

In the nebulous muck of life
Oh, the nebulous muck of life,
I've hardly a buoy, a berth, or a bailer,
Just neverending strife.

I pass many a vessel,
And each vessel passes me,
All guided by a different light
That seeks community.

With patience as an oar, that's right,
With patience as an oar,
We navigate each other
And exchange our journey's lore.

And should we choose to use our words
As tools and not for war,
Perhaps then that will be the day
At last we reach the shore.

HYPE GUY

He knew just how to raise the roof
On any given day,
Had photo albums filled with proof
From all his escapades.

He'd turn a courtroom scene
Into the hottest blacklight rave,
And yet, his kryptonite
Was being present near the grave.

THE UNDERTAKER

It could happen by accident
Driving your car
Or a fire that's lit by
Your late-night cigar.
You could drown in your bathtub
Or trip down the stairs.
You could camp in a forest
Surrounded by bears.
You could fall off a ladder,
A tree, or a cliff,
Sword fight with your outlet,
Get crushed by a fridge.
There are so many ways,
I could go on and on,
But the Undertaker
Is beginning to yawn.
See, to him, death's a bore
It is living that's hard,
With his stiffening back
From his work in the yard.
There's a daughter in college
He strains to support
And a single mother
He feels honored to court.

So, to poets and writers
Obsessed with the end,
Let's all spend some more time
In the land of pretend.
For the gritty and grimy
Mundane ev'ryday
Proves of much greater interest,
To him anyway.

THE ARTIST

The Artist sits atop a stool and speaks in platitudes
Of idiom and paradox; morals and attitudes.

The Artist says "The toughest words
Are sometimes none at all."
That "Those who flaunt how tall they are
Are actually quite small.

We're cold to one another 'cause we aren't warm to ourselves.
The people full of fear make even more of it themselves."

And on and on the Artist goes,
Streamlining walks of life
Until they're simplified locutions
Sharp as butter knives.

Even so, I'm grateful for the Artist and their works
That try to wrestle meaning from a world consumed with quirks.

The cool concrete of day-to-day
Can feel absent of twists,
But with the Artist there's a world
Where wonder still exists.

CHARLES

Grumpy
Gaunt
And gray old fart

Filthy mouth
Broke
Mother's heart

Sits alone
Slumped in his chair
Biting thoughts
Float through
The air

Soaked in grapes
An ashen cloud
Scribbling observations
Proud

Thanks,
You fought the urge to lie
I'll do my best
And never try.

WORK HORSE

Behind the smoke and mirrors
Of a well-accomplished show
Is a horse that bears no ribbons
Or makeup to help it glow.

A draft horse plowing on
Until it clocks out for the day,
Collapsing with a can of oats
Atop a bed of hay.

Without a brilliant saddle
Or a wreath of marigold,
This workhorse wakes up once again
To strain and break the mold.

The spotlight seldom falls upon
This horse and all its chores.
The mundane tasks of ev'ryday
Leave most observers bored.

If only they'd ignore
The equines eager to be seen,
They'd see the workhorse is the one
That really sets the scene.

OBITUARY

In the basement of a building
That can almost touch the sky
There hangs a golden placard
For a janitor who died.
The eulogy was written
In a leather treated chair
On the top floor by an intern
Scraping by to make bus fare.
The tribute was engraved
On foreign metal out of state,
And published with a signature
By some corporate magnate.
I happened on that gilded homage
Desperate for rapport,
And thought, "I hope I'm eulogized
By someone on my floor."

THE ONGOING SUMMIT OF ME

After twenty-nine years
I'm still grateful to know
That despite the ground covered
There's still much to go.

If you're willing to listen,
My foolish advice
Is to explore yourself
For your own paradise.

SUNSET

Well now, my friend,
Seems the day's nearly through.

So, it is,
But I'm glad I could share it with you.

Do you think there's a heaven?

I can't rightfully say...
If there is though,
I think I would prefer to stay.

What a crock of baloney.

Well frankly, it's true.
This moment's too lovely to bid it adieu.

Then I guess I can't leave.
I'll just sit here and wonder.

What's that?

How to make this all last a bit longer.

FARENHEIT 419

Entomb my work in shrouds of fire,
Let the lettering expire,
Words that were not mine to start
I stumbled upon in the dark.
For long after the ash has cleared,
When what I've said has disappeared,
They'll all still linger in the air
Adrift for someone else's snare.

PARTING NOTE

Whosoever finds this book
In any crevice, crack, or nook,
My hope is that these reveries
All serve as tiny remedies
To cure this thing called loneliness
A wicked bug that still persists.
We're not so different,
Ain't that great?
And where we are
Let's celebrate.

Ryan

Acknowledgments

To my family, friends, and all of those who helped keep me sane during the past two years: it didn't work, but thank you for trying!

To Charles Bukowski, Mike Mignola, and Shel Silverstein for their fearless works of inspiration.

To Aidan. I couldn't have done this without you, and more so, I wouldn't want to.

ABOUT THE AUTHOR

Ryan McCabe is an award-winning writer from Toledo, Ohio. A graduate of NYU's Tisch School of the Arts, his debut poetry collection "From the Bowels of My Heart" won the Indies Today Award for Best Humor Book. Additional poems of his have been published by Redivider, Poet's Choice, Wingless Dreamer, and Poetry Nation.

ABOUT THE ILLUSTRATOR

Aidan Terry is an animator and artist based in Los Angeles. His work has appeared in projects for HBO, Sony Pictures Animation, and Netflix. Two of the films to which he contributed, 2017's "Dear Basketball," and 2020's "Hair Love," won the Academy Award for Best Animated Short Film. He is currently working at Glen Keane Productions on a to-be-announced project.

$12.95
ISBN 978-1-7331663-9-3
51295>
9 781733 166393

Made in the USA
Middletown, DE
15 October 2022